# Collins

# SCRABBLE

BRAND CROSSWORD GAME

## junior

# Spelling
# Activity book

## Age 7-8

Published by Collins
An imprint of HarperCollinsPublishers
Westerhill Road
Bishopbriggs
Glasgow G64 2QT
www.harpercollins.co.uk

HarperCollinsPublishers
1st Floor, Watermarque Building, Ringsend Road, Dublin 4,
Ireland

© 2022 Mattel. SCRABBLE™ and SCRABBLE tiles, including S1
tiles, are trademarks of Mattel.

Collins ® is a registered trademark of HarperCollins Publishers
Limited

www.collins.co.uk

First published in 2022

© HarperCollins Publishers 2022

ISBN 978-0-00-852620-7

10 9 8 7 6 5 4 3 2 1

The contents of this publication are believed correct at the
time of printing. Nevertheless the publisher can accept no
responsibility for errors or omissions, changes in the detail
given or for any expense or loss thereby caused.

HarperCollins does not warrant that any website mentioned in
this title will be provided uninterrupted, that any website will
be error free, that defects will be corrected, or that the website
or the server that makes it available are free of viruses or bugs.
For full terms and conditions please refer to the site terms
provided on the website.

A catalogue record for this book is available from the British
Library

Printed in Great Britain by Martins the Printers

If you would like to comment on any aspect of this book, please
contact us at the above address or online.

E-mail: dictionaries@harpercollins.co.uk

f facebook.com/collinsdictionary
🐦 @collinsdict

ACKNOWLEDGEMENTS
All images © Shutterstock.com

# UNSCRAMBLE!

Can you use the picture clues to help you unscramble these words?

n u r ☐☐☐

m s w i ☐☐☐☐

e s l m i ☐☐☐☐☐

t n i k ☐☐☐☐

d e n g a r ☐☐☐☐☐☐

y r c ☐☐☐

n i w ☐☐☐

# ADD -ING

Now add the ending -ing to each word you have unscrambled. Write the new word, making any spelling changes, in the grid.

What is the word ending in -ing in the pink squares running down?

Can you find these words ending in -ing in the word search below?

| | | |
|---|---|---|
| spinning | finishing | beginning |
| digging | wetting | bobbing |
| living | popping | |

g d w g p o v g g w
n n g f y i z n p n e
i z n i q i p s i t
n s b i g t p l b t
n l c g p i q c b i
i p i m n p w k o n
g d j n l g o h b g
e k i l z e j p b y
b n l i v i n g s v
g g n i h s i n i f

One word in the wordsearch ended with the letter 'e' before the -ing ending was added. Write that word here.

- - - - - - - - - - - - - - - - - - - - - -

# NEVER END -ED

Add the ending -ed to each word on the left. Remember to make any spelling changes. The first one has been done for you.

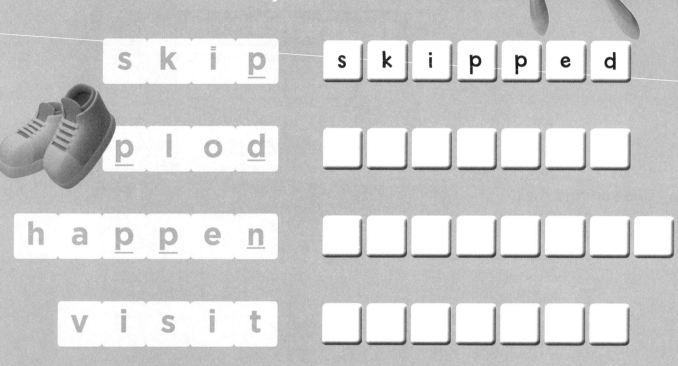

| skip | | s k i p p e d |
|------|---|---------------|
| plod | | |
| happen | | |
| visit | | |
| admit | | |

Tick the word in each pair that has been correctly spelt with the -ed ending.

darkened

darkenned

saddened

saddenned

corrected

corretted

# ADDING -ATION

Can you add the ending -ation to these verbs to make nouns? The first one has been done for you.

c r e a t e

| c | r | e | a | t | i | o | n |

a d m i r e

| | | | | | | | | | |

p r e p a r e

| | | | | | | | | | | |

i n d i c a t e

| | | | | | | | | | | |

s e n s e

| | | | | | | | | |

a d o r e

| | | | | | | | |

d o n a t e

| | | | | | | |

# MAKING NEW WORDS

Choose the correct letters from the circle to complete the words. Letters can be used more than once. Tip: Do the ones you know first.

☐ ☐ c o r r e c t

☐ ☐ ☐ c o n t i n u e

☐ ☐ c o n n e c t

d i s

u n   i n

r e m i s

☐ ☐ d e c o r a t e

☐ ☐ ☐ a g r e e

☐ ☐ a w a r e

☐ ☐ a c t i v e

☐ ☐ ☐ s p e l l

# GIVE US A CLUE

Use the clues to complete the tiles with words starting with the letters dis-, mis-, un-, and re-.

**To vanish**

☐ ☐ ☐ ☐ ☐ ☐ ☐ ☐ ☐

**An adjective meaning sad**

☐ ☐ ☐ ☐ ☐ ☐ ☐

**Heat up again**

☐ ☐ ☐ ☐ ☐ ☐

**The opposite of obey**

☐ ☐ ☐ ☐ ☐ ☐ ☐

**To behave badly**

☐ ☐ ☐ ☐ ☐ ☐ ☐ ☐ ☐ ☐

**To appear again**

☐ ☐ ☐ ☐ ☐ ☐ ☐ ☐

# BACK-TO-FRONT AND UPSIDE DOWN!

The following six words are adjectives which have been written back-to-front or upside down. Write them correctly in the blank tiles beside each one, then turn them into adverbs by adding the letters –ly.

1. t e i u q

2. t c i r t s

3. t n e i t a p

4. l a n i f

5. m l a c

6. y d e e r g

**4.** ☐☐☐☐☐☐☐

**5.** ☐☐☐☐☐☐

**6.** ☐☐☐☐☐☐☐☐

# MAKING ADVERBS

Use the picture clues to help you complete
the missing adverbs ending in -ly.

Slow down! I can't walk that **q**☐☐☐☐☐☐!

Make sure you
write your name **n**☐☐☐☐☐ on the paper.

Hold the baby very **c**☐☐☐☐☐☐☐☐.

It's important to dress

**w a**☐☐☐☐ when it's cold outside.

Check your answers when you have

**c o m p**☐☐☐☐☐☐ finished.

# ONE + ONE = ONE

Some words are made up of two separate words.
They are called compound words.

c l a s s + r o o m = c l a s s r o o m

Draw a line from each word on the left to its 'partner' on the right to make a compound word. Use the picture sums to help you.

| | |
|---|---|
| t o a d | c a k e |
| s u n | b r u s h |
| p a n | n a i l |
| l a d y | s t o o l |
| t o o t h | k n o b |
| f i n g e r | b i r d |
| d o o r | f l o w e r |

t □□□■□□□□

s □■□□□□□□

p □□■□□□□

l □□□□■□□□□

t □□□□□□□□■□□

d □□■□□□□□□

f □□□□□■□□□□

Now write each compound word that you have created in the grid. Write the compound word formed from the letters in the pink boxes on the line below.

□□□□□□□

## CONNECTIONS

These compound words have been joined incorrectly! Can you undo them and write them correctly in the boxes below?

l i g h t r o b <u>e</u>

c <u>u</u> p <u>b</u> u l <u>b</u>

e y e s h e l f

w a r d <u>b</u> o a r <u>d</u>

b <u>o</u> o k <u>b</u> o o k

<u>n</u> o t e l a s h

l □□□□□□□□

c □□□□□□□□

e □□□□□□□

w □□□□□□□

b □□□□□□□

n □□□□□□□

11

# ENOUGH IS ENOUGH!

Can you solve the clues to find words with an 'uh' sound spelt 'ou'? Write your answers in the squares next to each.

When you are not old.

The opposite to half.

You might get into this if you are naughty!

When you feel something with your fingertips.

The opposite of smooth.

The child of your mum or dad's sister or brother.

# FASCINATING 'S' SOUND

Can you unscramble these letters to make words with an 's' sound spelt 'sc'?

s e c r e c n t

c s n e r y e

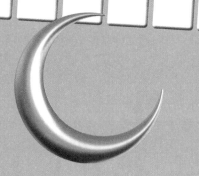

s s s s i c r o

12

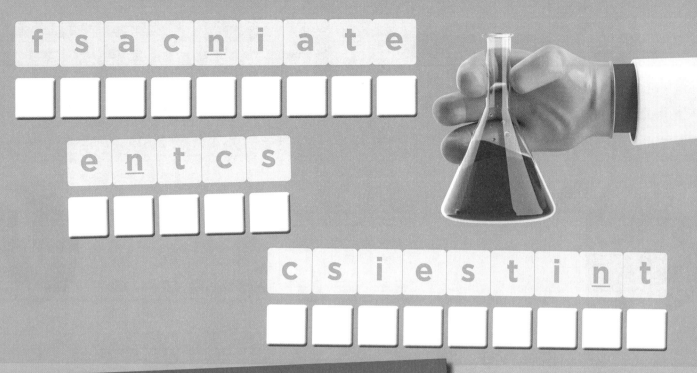

f s a c n i a t e

e n t c s

c s i e s t i n t

# UP, UP AND AWAY!

Solve the clues then write the missing letters to complete each word.
All the words have an 'ay' sound spelt either 'ei', 'eigh' or 'ey'.

To do as you are told.

o _ _ y

When you measure how heavy something is.

w _ _ _ h

This carries blood to your heart.

v _ _ n

Someone who lives next door to you.

n _ _ _ _ _ _ o u r

Straps that helps you guide a horse.

r _ _ _ s

What we call an animal eaten by another animal.

p _ _ y

The number after seven.

e _ _ _ t

The colour you get when you add white to black.

g _ _ _

13

# WHY NOT?

Say the words in the box out loud. They all contain the letter 'y'. Can you find them in the wordsearch below?

| | |
|---|---|
| myth | python |
| pyramid | symbol |
| oxygen | prayer |
| style | tyre |
| royal | gymnast |

```
m y t h b q c c o s
r p y t h o n h m y
o r p y r a m i d m
y a m i p u i s g b
a y n n a n s h y o
l e u a s e t i m l
n r n b t k m t n y
u s k t y a a y a a
s t g m l i s r s n
o x y g e n n e t o
```

# PICTURE CLUES

Use the pictures to help you complete the words that contain the letter 'y'.

t □ □ □ e

c □ □ □ □ l □ □

c □ □ □ e

c □ □ □ □ □ □ r

# WORD DETECTIVE

The words below have shorter words hidden inside them. The letters are in the correct order. For example:

m a c h i **n** e
c h i n

Can you find more names of parts of the body in these words, then write them in the squares below?

c h a i r
□ □ □ □

a s k i **n** g
□ □ □ □

s l i **p** **p** e r
□ □ □

**d** r e a r y
□ □ □

o **b** e y e **d**
□ □ □

s h i **n** i **n** g
□ □ □ □

w h i **p** **p** i **n** g
□ □ □

c h a r m i **n** g
□ □ □

s **n** a i l
□ □ □

# SOUNDS THE SAME

Some words sound the same but are spelt differently. The pairs of words below have been written back-to-front. Can you write each one correctly? The first one has been done for you.

r a e **b**     **b** e a r

e r a **b**     **b** a r e

e r i t     ☐ ☐ ☐ ☐

e r y t     ☐ ☐ ☐ ☐

e t i r w     ☐ ☐ ☐ ☐ ☐

t h g i r     ☐ ☐ ☐ ☐ ☐

e o t     ☐ ☐ ☐

w o t     ☐ ☐ ☐

t e e m     ☐ ☐ ☐ ☐

t a e m     ☐ ☐ ☐ ☐

Can you complete each sentence below with the correct spelling of each word from page 16?

Grandpa began to _____ after a long day in the garden.

Mum needed to replace the punctured _____ on her car.

The big, brown _____ climbed to the top of the tree.

My _____ legs were cold in the icy rain.

Sheba said she would _____ to me from Australia.

Freddie used the _____ code to open the door.

I banged my _____ on the step.

Dad had to _____ Gran's car to the garage.

Harry said it was great to _____ the famous footballer.

My big sister has stopped eating _____.

# GIVE US A CLUE

Use the picture clues to help find one missing word from each puzzle. The second word sounds like the first word but has a different spelling. One has been done for you.

m a i l   o _ _

a

l

e

b _ _ _

r _ _ _

h _ _ l

_

_

_

l

# ARE YOU SURE IT'S SURE?

The words below end in either -sure or -ture. You might want to use a dictionary to help you fill in the missing endings.

f u r n i [ ] [ ] [ ]

e n c l o [ ] [ ] [ ]

m e a [ ] [ ] [ ]

a d v e n [ ] [ ] [ ] [ ]

p l e a [ ] [ ] [ ]

p i c [ ] [ ] [ ] [ ]

n a [ ] [ ] [ ] [ ]

c r e a [ ] [ ] [ ]

18

Now write each word in the correct column.

| -sure ending | -ture ending |
| --- | --- |
| | |

# WORDS FROM WORDS

Can you make six 3-letter words using the 5 letters on the right? There are some pictures to help you with some of the words.

Now try making six more 3-letter words with these letters.

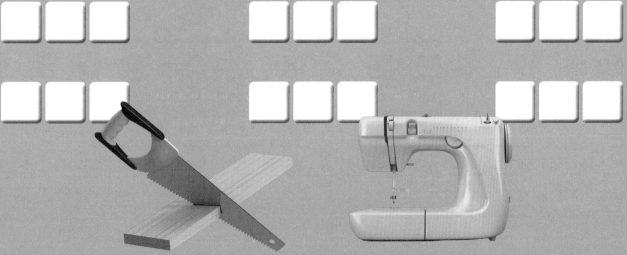

# CODE WORDS

Can you crack this secret code? Look at the signs below the boxes, and fill in the right letters to solve the message.

| a | b | c | d | e | f | g | h | i | j | k | l | m |
|---|---|---|---|---|---|---|---|---|---|---|---|---|

| n | o | p | q | r | s | t | u | v | w | x | y | z |
|---|---|---|---|---|---|---|---|---|---|---|---|---|

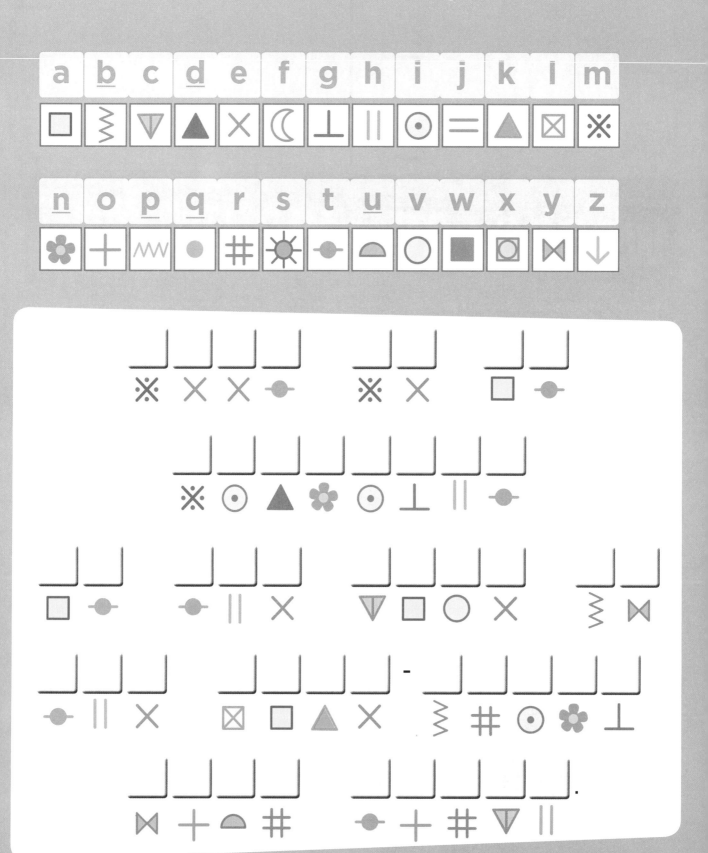

# RHYMING WORDS

Use the letters in the circles to make a word that rhymes with the word in the squares.

c l o u d

s t u m b l e

s p r e a d

b r o w n

a n c i e n t

b a n i s h

# MORE RHYMING WORDS

Use the letters in the circles to make a word that
rhymes with the word in the squares.

r
s
e
v
w

s
a
p
t
e
r
a

**c** **u** **r** **v** **e**

**d** **e** **s** **p** **e** **r** **a** **t** **e**

a
i
f

h
e
z
e
w

**b** **e** **a** **r**

**s** **e** **i** **z** **e**

r
a
a
b
e

o
p
d
r
a

**w** **e** **i** **r** **d**

**g** **a** **r** **d** **e** **n**

# HIDDEN WORDS

Add letters at the end of the first word in each pair to the letters at the beginning of the second word to make a new, 4-letter word. One has been done for you. Watch out – some have more than one possible answer!

dri**ve** **st**airs — **vest**

hidin**g** **o**lder —

moist **o**perate —

leav**e** **i**nland —

flam**e** **a**lways —

ech**o** **p**ear —

cris**p** **i**nto —

**p**in**c**h **o**pera —

**t**unnel **a**w**n**ing —

# SHUN FUN

The sound 'shun' at the end of words can be spelt either -tion, -cian, -sion or -ssion. Use the picture clues to help you complete the words in the circles which end in -tion or -cian.

-tion

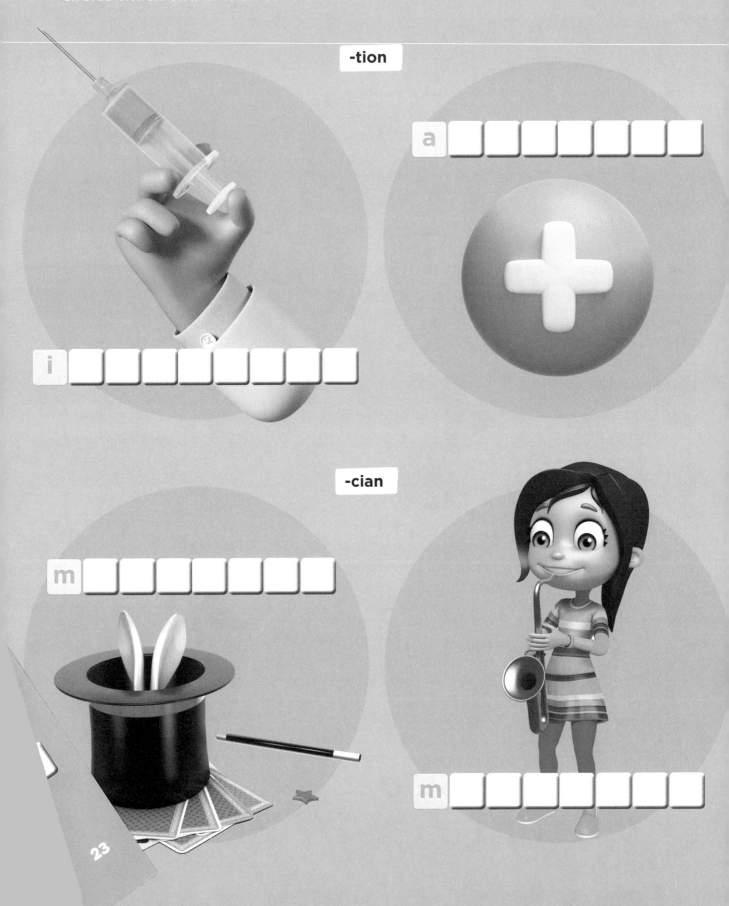

a▢▢▢▢▢▢▢

i▢▢▢▢▢▢▢▢

-cian

m▢▢▢▢▢▢▢

m▢▢▢▢▢▢

Add the endings -ssion or -sion to the words below. Do they take -ssion or -sion? Tip: look at the ending of each word that has been done for you: process, permit and extend.

possess     commit
permit     suspend
discuss     admit
extend     process
confess     transmit
comprehend     expand

**-ssion**

p r o c e s s i o n

p e r m i s s i o n

TICKET

**-sion**

e x t e n s i o n

25

# PROPER NOUNS

In the game of Junior Scrabble, you are not allowed to use proper nouns, so it is a good idea to know what these are! Proper nouns begin with a capital letter and include the following: names of people, places, countries, continents, oceans, planets, days of the week and months of the year.

Can you find 10 proper nouns in this word search? Write them in the squares on the opposite page, remembering to start each one with a capital letter.

```
j   w   p   i   t   e   m   a   y   i
m   e   g   y   p   t   o   t   w   m
r   e   n   g   l   a   n   d   o   o
m   q   t   u   e   s   d   a   y   n
a   y   t   h   f   r   a   y   y   d
r   c   d   j   u   l   y   x   g   a
s   j   s   u   a   i   n   r   e   n
w   e   d   n   e   s   d   a   y   j
e   t   c   e   a   l   h   y   q   k
```

**Here are some clues:**

- a country that is next to Scotland
- a country famous for its pyramids
- a boy's three-letter name
- three months of the year
- three days of the week
- a planet.

26

# SSHHHH! SILENT LETTERS

Can you finish the words below with their missing silent letters?

s _ i e n t i s t

_ n o m e

c o m _

_ r a p p e r

_ h o l e

t h u m _

_ o u r

_ n i t t i n g

r e i _ n

w _ i s _ l e

l i s _ e n

# FINISH AND START

Add the same letter to the end of each partial word on the left and the beginning of each partial word on the right to make two real words. The first two have been done for you.

| b | u | i | l | d | i | n | **g** | | **g** | r | u | m | p | y |

| | s | n | o | ☐ | | | ☐ | e | a | t | h | e | r |

| | b | o | l | ☐ | | | ☐ | u | n | g | e | o | n |

| | l | a | w | ☐ | | | ☐ | i | b | b | l | e |

| t | h | i | n | ☐ | | | ☐ | n | i | t |

| s | p | a | c | ☐ | | | ☐ | v | e | n |

| | c | r | a | z | ☐ | | | ☐ | o | u | n | g |

| | c | a | m | e | ☐ | | | ☐ | a | b | e | l |

| f | l | o | a | ☐ | | | ☐ | o | a | d |

| | l | a | m | ☐ | | | ☐ | a | l | d |

29

# CROSSWORD

Can you use the clues on the page opposite to solve the crossword? The letters in the squares highlighted in pink spell a nocturnal animal. Unjumble them and write the name of the animal in the squares at the bottom of the page. (If you're not sure what 'nocturnal' means, look it up in your dictionary.)

## ACROSS

1.  a black and white bear

3.  something you clean with a mop

5.  a joint between your leg and your foot

6.  a bird with a red breast

7.  something you do to get an answer

8.  means the same as 'listened'

10. a place to sit to stay cool when it is sunny

12. an animal found in the desert

14. the sound a sheep makes; an anagram of 'table'

16. a wise bird of the night

17. not ever

18. change something

19. when you've finished drinking, your cup is _ _ _ _ _

20. the planet humans live on

## DOWN

1.  a juicy fruit

2.  in front

3.  go with knives on the table

4.  a selection of something

9.  part of your body attached to your shoulder

11. a primate, very similar to a monkey

12. unscramble the word 'ocean' to find this small, narrow boat

13. a large vehicle used for transport

14. a small piece of grass

15. a small, hand-held light

# ANSWERS

**Page 2**
run, swim, smile, knit, garden, cry, win

**Page 3**

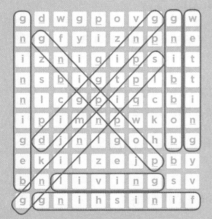

live → living

**Page 4**
plodded, happened, visited, admitted

darkened, saddened, corrected

**Page 5**
admiration, preparation, indication, sensation, adoration, donation

**Page 6**
incorrect, discontinue, reconnect, redecorate, disagree, unaware, inactive, misspell

**Page 7**
disappear, unhappy, reheat, disobey, misbehave, reappear

**Pages 8-9**
1. quiet, 2. strict, 3. patient, 4. final, 5. calm, 6. greedy

1. quietly, 2. strictly, 3. patiently, 4. finally, 5. calmly, 6. greedily

**Page 9**
quickly, neatly, carefully, warmly, completely

**Page 10**
toadstool, sunflower, pancake, ladybird, toothbrush, fingernail, doorknob

**Page 11**
Ensure the words from page 10 have been spelt correctly.
SUNBURN is the word formed from the letters in the pink boxes.

lightbulb, cupboard, eyelash, wardrobe, bookshelf, notebook

**Page 12-13**
young, double, trouble, touch, rough, cousin, crescent, scenery, scissors, fascinate, scent, scientist

**Page 13**
obey, weigh, vein, neighbour, reins, prey, eight, grey

**Page 14**

type, cymbal, cycle, cylinder

**Page 15**
hair, skin, lip, ear, eye, shin, hip, arm, nail

**Page 16**
tire, tyre; write, right; toe, tow; meet, meat

**Page 17**
Grandpa began to tire after a long day in the garden.

Mum needed to replace the punctured tyre on her car.

The big, brown bear climbed to the top of the tree.

My bare legs were cold in the icy rain.

Sheba said she would write to me from Australia.

Freddie used the right code to open the door.

I banged my toe on the step.

Dad had to tow Gran's car to the garage.

Harry said it was great to meet the famous footballer.

My big sister has stopped eating meat.

oar, or; blew, blue; rain, rein; heel, heal

**Pages 18-19**
The words should be written in the correct column and spelt correctly.

-sure ending:
enclosure,
measure,
pleasure

-ture ending:
furniture,
adventure,
picture, nature, creature

**Page 19**
ten, tin, win, nit, wet, net, new, tie, wit; was, wag, sew, saw, gas, sea, awe, age sag

**Page 20**
Meet me at midnight at the cave by the lake – bring your torch.

**Page 21**
cloud, aloud; stumble, fumble; spread, bread; brown, town; ancient, patient; banish, vanish

**Page 22**
curve, swerve; desperate, separate; bear, fair; seize, wheeze; weird, beard; garden, pardon

**Page 23**
gold, stop, vein, meal, chop or hope, spin or pint, chop or hope, lawn

**Page 24**
addition, injection, magician, musician

**Page 25**
discussion, confession, possession, transmission, commission, admission, expansion, comprehension, suspension

**Page 26**

**Page 27**
Mars, July, May, Wednesday, Dan, Monday, June, England, Tuesday, Egypt

**Page 28**
scientist, gnome, comb, wrapper, whole, thumb, hour, knitting, reign, whistle, listen

**Page 29**
snow, weather; bold, dungeon; lawn, nibble; think, knit; space, even; crazy, young; camel, label; float, toad; lamb, bald

**Page 30-31**

Nocturnal animal: badger

32